Book One

Simon Goes to Turkey

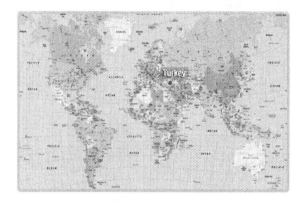

By Andrea Wetzel

For Henry and Emma

Prologue

My name is Simon. Simon Sez. Yeah, it's a real riot. Ha ha. My parents are weird. They named my sister Who. Get it? Who Sez. I told you, they're weird. What's even weirder are their jobs. Well, my mom's job. My dad is a novelist. Only he hasn't ever written anything except one time he wrote this really long grocery list and my mom got mad because it had a bunch of stuff on it we didn't need and so they hollered about the price of tea in China, whatever that means, and then he stopped writing grocery lists and going to the store. My mom has a cool job, though. She works for a local TV station and travels all over the world doing what she calls 'human interest' stories. Basically, that means if something is going on in the world that makes a lot of people happy or mad or sad, she goes and drags us with her... my parents thought it would be good for us to be students of the world. I told you, they're weirdos. I have seen some pretty cool stuff, though. I'm only ten and I've been to over seven countries....that's almost one a year because my mom said you can't count the early years because I was still in diapers and she's not crazy enough to take a baby to a country that might not sell Huggies. So it wasn't until I was about three that we started to really travel. My dad calls it globe trotting. I had heard of the Harlem Globetrotters, but this isn't the same. We literally go all over the world and hang out, sometimes for a month, sometimes for a week, whatever. However long it takes for her to 'get the story'.

I'm in the 4th grade at Winchester Elementary. My dumb sister Who is going into preschool next year. Those teachers don't know what they're in for. They had me and I was pretty awesome, so they are going to be surprised that we're even related. They'll probably want to have me come back and give me some award or something for putting up with her every day.

Chapter 1

Last night my mom told me we were going to
Turkey. And I'm not talking about a gobble-
gobble kind of turkey; I'm talking about the
country. Yeah, there's a country called Turkey,
can you believe that? I wonder if they have a
town called Chicken? Ha ha. I have to make
jokes to make myself laugh because my sister
Who doesn't ever make jokes and otherwise,
who else is going to crack me up? Well, I have a
friend, Joey, who sometimes makes me laugh
but really, he only cracked me up once...and that
was because he stepped in dog poop with bare
feet and it squished between his toes and he
freaked out like a chicken. I wonder if he'd be
more comfortable in Turkey since he acts like a
chicken. See? I crack myself up.

Whenever mom tells us we're going somewhere,
my sister always has a million questions. How
long is it going to take? How long will we be
there? Can she bring her stuffed animals? Do
they sell Orangie Orange Soda wherever we're
going? Because if there is one thing my sister
won't do, is go anywhere without her stuffed
puppy, Lovey or anywhere that doesn't sell that
stupid drink. Me? I like root beer. That's the

only pop my mom is ok with me drinking because she says it doesn't have caffeine. My mom has a thing about kids and caffeine.   Of course, I think that's stupid because it has so much sugar in it, who cares about a little caffeine? Although one time I had a few Cokes and couldn't sleep for a long time…it's a good thing I have a dog to talk to in the middle of the night…but usually she sleeps with her butt in my face so I'm really talking to her butt. Sometimes she'll answer me with a huge fart.

Chapter 2

"What's too-key like, Sissy?" Who asked me.

"Mom! Who keeps calling me Sissy!" My mom really needed to get a handle on this. Who had been calling me Sissy since she was a baby and it was ok when she was really little but now it was starting to make me mad. Especially when she said it in front of my friends.

"Well, Simon, that's what she always has called you...remember how hard it was for her to say your name? It's kind of a habit now." With that, my mom wiped Who's nose and kept telling her to "Blow! Blow!" I don't know what is wrong with my sister...who doesn't know how to blow their own nose?
"You like to call brother Sissy, don't you?" my mom was nuts...she started to blow on Who's stomach, making her laugh and blow a big snot bubble out of her nose. Gross.

"MOM! I don't WANT her to call me that anymore! It's embarrassing!" I raised my voice, which I'm not really supposed to do, but this was getting ridiculous.

"Ok, ok, Simon. We'll work on it. OK...Who? From now on, let's remember to call Simon, Simon and NOT Sissy, ok?"

Who looked at my mom and me for a long time. Then she tilted her head to the side and said, "Who says?"

My mom tilted her head to the side, too. "I say. No more Sissy. It's Simon."

"Says Who?" I could tell what that little smart alek was doing.

"Who says his name is Sissy!" and then she started to laugh so hard her face turned bright red.

"Who! I know you think this is funny, but we really need to be respectful of Simon's wishes. You're a big girl now and you know how to say Simon, so no more Sissy." I kind of hated it when my mom started babbling about being respectful. That kid needed a smack.

"OK, then, Simon, grab your backpack, Who put on your jacket. We need to go to school to talk to them about our trip and I want to be early." My

8

mom walked out of the room, looking for her keys.

"Sissy? You dinint say what is too-key like."

"How should I know? We haven't been there yet, remember? Ugh. Look, I saw on TV once they make ice cream out of orchids. Now leave me alone."

"Sissy? What's a orkid?"

"Flowers...like those..." and I pointed to some silk orchids my mom had on our coffee table and went to find my backpack.

"SIMON!!!"

"What?!" I ran back downstairs.

"What is the meaning of this?" My mom asked and pointed to my sister...who in the few minutes my mom had been looking for her keys and I had gone upstairs to get my back pack, was sitting on the living room floor, surrounded by little cut up pieces of silk orchids and right in between her legs was a half eaten container of MY mint chocolate chip ice cream...she was smooshing the fake flowers she had cut up in MY ice cream and eating it.

"What the???" and I glared at Who. It was one thing to call me Sissy when no one was around, but to ruin MY ice cream?

"Sissy says in Too-key they have o-kid ice crweam...I'm making it for us." She held up a wooden spoon, full of MY ice cream and silk flower pieces.

"Well...yes, Turkey does do that BUT you know better! No ice cream for breakfast!" WHAT??? Sometimes I think my mom is crazy.

"Uh, Mom? How about no eating MY ice cream for breakfast?? And shouldn't she get in trouble for cutting up that dumb plant?" Why did I have to be the one to explain this??

When we got to school, my mom and Who came into my classroom with me. Great. Booger Welsh was already there. Also known as Brandon, but I called him Booger in my head cause he was such a jerk. He had all the teachers fooled, too. They all thought he was sooo great.

"Mrs. King? May I have a word? Another trip has come up..." my mom smiled at my teacher. "Simon, watch Who."

Who walked over to me, where I was TRYING to ignore her because I knew that dumb Booger Welsh was watching.

"Sissy?"
I glared at her.

"Sissy?"

I glared even harder.

"SISSY!!!!!! DO YOU NEED HEARING RAIDS???? I'M TALKING TO YOU!"

"WHAT?"

"Hi." Then the little brat walked away.

I didn't want to look. But I had to.

Turned my face toward Booger...he had his lips all sucked in and his chest was moving up and down like he was trying really hard not to laugh.

I studied his face. Hoped he didn't hear…then he walked over to me.

"Simon?"

"Hey..what's up Brandon?"
And then he burst out laughing and ran into the hallway. I could hear other kids laughing…then I heard what sounded like a million voices say "Good Morning, SISSY"
We couldn't get to Turkey fast enough.

Chapter 3

Whenever we fly anywhere, I get ginger ale. My mom never buys it, but for some reason, she lets me have it when we are on a plane...I don't get it. So while I was drinking my fourth ginger ale, my mom started talking about the different kinds of food in Turkey.

"I'm sure we will have all kinds of baklava" she said.

I didn't really know what that was but I didn't really care...right now I just needed to pee...Who seemed to be really confused, which wasn't a surprise, that kid was confused about everything.

When I got back from the bathroom, Who started bugging me about baklava.

"Sissy? What's barking lava?"

"It's a weird dessert...only in Turkey....when you get it, it might look like a little cake or something...but it's NOT! You need to bark at it, REALLY loud, or it will come to life and melt your face off....like lava....get it? So YOU bark at the

barking lava so it doesn't turn into lava and
dissolve you into a big puddle of goo."

Who looked terrified. I smiled to myself and
drank some more ginger ale. Served her right for
calling me Sissy in front of that idiot Booger
Welsh. I buzzed the little button for the lady to
come over...we had at least another five hours
on this flight and I was going to drink as much
ginger ale as I could hold.

Chapter 4

Istanbul is huge...and noisy. The people were super nice, though. We got up really, really early and I was already sweaty. I hoped there would be someplace to swim or at least that our hotel would have air conditioning...it was really hot out.

First thing we were supposed to do was go to the Grand Bazaar, where my mom was going to talk to some old lady about her rugs. My mom said people in Turkey are famous for their rugs...not like Lady Gaga famous, but famous enough I guess. This one lady had been making rugs for a super long time and her fingers were are twisted up and she was like a million years old or something but still made these rugs and sold them at this place called the Grand Bazaar, which my mom said was huge and had over 5,000 little shops in it and this one lady had been in the same shop for a really long time, just making rugs with her weird looking hands. For whatever reason, she was who my mom was doing a story on...if it had been me, I would have done a story on windsurfing or scuba diving or something cool but whatever.

The Grand Bazaar was crazy. There were tons, and I mean TONS of people and they were selling crazy stuff...lots of rugs, which people were making a big deal about, spices that my mom kept freaking out about and lots of stores that sold different kinds of pottery. I saw a store named Aladdin that had a bunch of brass oil lamps.

"Hey, Who...look in there...see all those weird pitcher things? Remind you of anything?" I asked.

"What?" She looked in the shop.

"What are those?"

"Well, that's a genie store. Remember Aladdin & Jasmine? Well, this is where people in Turkey get their genies...everyone has one."
Sometimes messing with my sister was too easy. Who's eyes got really big...I watched as her eyes looked up and saw the Aladdin sign...then she screamed.

"Ahhh!!! Genie! I need a genie!" Then she ran into the shop and started rubbing the lamps. The guy who owned the shop looked nervous, like she was going to break a bunch of stuff, but my dad got to her before she did any real damage.

"Where's Abu??" Who asked the store guy.

"What? I'm sorry, young girl, I don't know..."

Who kept looking around the store, like her eyes were trying to follow a fly or something...she looked like a lunatic.

"You know...ABU!! Aladdin's monkey!! WHERE IS HE?????"

My dad started to do that weird laugh he does when he doesn't really know what to say. He smiled at the guy and held on to Who's hand.

"Very sorry, she's confused. Not sure why she thinks…." Then my dad looked at me.

"Simon?"

"Yes?"

"Any idea why Who thinks Abu is in this store?"

"um…well, I uh…ok, fine. I told her it was Aladdin's store. Which it IS, right?"

"That's enough Simon. We'll talk about this later and I'm taking your DS for the night. Let's go, kids. Again, sorry, sir."

We walked back out into the market place and found my mom.

"Oh, isn't this wonderful? I love this place! So rich in culture."
I rolled my eyes. So far, I was hot, hungry and had gotten in trouble for a simple practical joke. My mom could tell I wasn't happy.

"Simon? I have some more research to do...why don't you three just take in the Grand Bazaar NICELY...if we don't have any more problems, maybe we can go swimming tomorrow?"

"Yes!!! Does our hotel have a pool??? That would be awesome!"

My mom just smiled at my dad, like they were part of some secret.

The next morning, I grabbed my swimming trunks right away.

"Ready! Are we going?" I yelled. Grabbed my goggles and started looking around for a towel.

"OK, just throw a shirt on...we are actually going to the beach..."

AWESOME....this was even better. I couldn't wait.

Chapter 5

As we waited for the shuttle to pick us up, I started to get hungry, even though I had just eaten breakfast. My mom swears I have a tape worm which I guess means I can eat a lot or that I have some weird worm who's eating all my food. If I did, I think I'd name it Ralph.

There was a candy store right by the hotel and I really wanted to go...my goal was to try every kind of candy; I mean, if I have to leave my friends, my Xbox, sour patch kids and my dog, they should let me have how ever much candy I want.

"Mom? Can we go to that candy store?"

"No, Simon, our shuttle is coming...maybe when we get back."

"Puuullleeeezzzeeee????? I'm starving!"

My mom pulled out an apple to me to take.

Ugh.

"I'm not hungry for THAT. I'm hungry for candy. Maybe they have ORANGIE ORANGE, too." I said it just loud enough for Who to hear. She did.

My mom gave me that one look that says she knows what I just did but before she could say anything, Who was freaking out.

"MOMMY? I NEEEEEEEED ORANGIE ORANGE!!!!! PUHLEEZE!!!! I WILL SHARE WIFF YOU! YOU CAN PET LOVEY! I WILL DIE IF WE DON'T GO THERE RIGHT NOW!"

"I don't think the shuttle will be here for at least twenty minutes. Why don't you take them?" My dad asked my mom as he leaned back on the bench and closed his eyes.

"I'll just catch a few winks."

"Uh, I don't think so. Nice try. You take them and I will wait for the shuttle..." then I swear she muttered "in peace." Jeez, like taking us to the candy store was such a big deal.

Who and I were both staring at my dad like my dog stares at me when I'm eating a really good cheeseburger. I think he knew we were going and he was taking us. Surprisingly, he didn't look very happy about it, which I thought was weird, because who doesn't love going to the candy store?

When we walked it, I noticed an old lady behind the counter. She had a scarf on her head and a super wrinkly face that was really tan. She smiled at my sister and me.

"Hos geldiniz! Bon bon?"

I didn't know what the first part meant, but I new that bon bon meant candy...I started nodding my head. Who just copied me and started bouncing her head up and down too.

"American?"

We kept nodding.

"Ah! I speak....little..English....you like candy, yes?" We just kept nodding like idiots.

She clapped her hands together and motioned for us to sit on a little bench next to the counter.

"I tell story!" She pinched my cheeks with both hands then turned to Who and did the same thing.

"You try Turkish Delight?"

This time, we shook our heads.

"Ah, wonderful! You try, you try! But first, I tell story! Sit! Sit!" she motioned, again, to the little bench. Finally, we sat down.

"One time, long, long ago, in the time of Sultans, there was a candy maker...he's name Hac Bekir....he come from the mountains by the sea to Istanbul to make he's sweets and oh, the people loved these! One day, the sultan, tired of hard candy, tried the sweets Hac Bekir was making for the people and he was so happy to have a soft candy that will no hurt his tooth!"

Then she clapped her hands and pointed to her teeth. "He's candy called Turkish Delight...we call it lokum....it is very soft, very good...you will like..."

She quickly walked behind the counter and came back with two light pink squares of candy.

"Try! Try!"

I took a bite. It kind of tasted like a super soft gummy bear. It was good, though. It was kind of chewy, really sweet and covered in sugar.

Who popped the whole thing in her mouth.

The lady looked at us, waiting to see what we thought.

"Well? You like?"

"Yes..thanks." I had such good manners. Who, on the other hand, was still busy chewing; it looked like she wanted to say something but had too much in her mouth. She kept slapping her hands on her knees, like that would make her swallow it faster or something. When she finally did, she blurted out: "do you have Orangie Orange soda???"

The lady looked confused and shook her head.

"No, young miss...but I have tea! I put in lots of sugar for you!" She handed Who a cup of lukewarm tea; it must have had a ton of sugar in it, because she drank it really fast. Then she held out her cup..."More?"

"Ah! Wonderful! Yes, young miss, more!" In about five minutes, my sister drank about four cups of tea.
I was only kind of paying attention, because I was checking out the different kinds of Turkish Delight...thinking I would get a couple of green ones for Joey and tell him they were booger candy. He'd crack up.

My dad had been talking to another man in the shop about the history of Turkish Delight, how the guy in the story had a store almost three hundred years ago and it was still there today, still selling candy. I thought that was pretty cool.

My dad and I noticed Who about the same time....her eyes were really wide open, like she was trying to pop them out of her head and she kept licking the ring of powdered sugar that was on her mouth.

"Dad? Who had some tea...that has caffeine, right?"

"Oh...no...how much did she have??"

We both looked at my sister, who was holding up four fingers. We looked at each other. This wasn't good.

Chapter 6

"How'd it go?" My mom asked.

"Good! Mommy, I had a bunch of tea and sugar and candy and I need more candy and I really like tea and Sissy told me I need to stop talking so fast but I really liked that candy and I want more candy and all the flavors and they didn't have Orangie Orange but we had a sto-wee and the lady I bet is a grandma and she let me have so much tea!" Then she stopped for a second to breath.

"You let her have four cups of tea? Of caffeinated tea, right before we take a long shuttle ride?" My mom looked at my dad like she wanted to cry.

My parents, well, mostly my mom, decided we would take the later shuttle and have lunch at a restaurant by our hotel. She didn't think it was a good idea to take my sister, who was acting like a wind up hamster, on an hour-long bus ride without letting some of the caffeine wear off.

My lunch was awesome. I don't know what it was, but it was really good. Some kind of meat sandwich but not roast beef…I was definitely gonna get another one of these while we were here, they were way better than the tuna sandwiches my mom made.

While we were eating our lunch, my mom started talking about our trip to the beach. We were going to the Black Sea…even if the water wasn't black, it sounded cool. She also told me that we were going to take a ferry and see how Turkey connects Europe to Asia, kind of like a bridge. She also told me we were going to a place called Cappadocia that looked kind of like the moon. I was starting to think of funny pictures we could take…like I could stick an American flag in the ground like that Armstrong guy, when the baklava came.

"WOOF! WOOF! WOOOOFFFFF!!! WOOF! WOOF! WOOOOOOOOOOOOOOOOFFFF!!!" Who had jumped on her chair and was barking at her plate.

Oh…..no.

My mom and dad kept telling her to calm down, and finally my dad stood up and carried her outside…she kept barking the whole way out.

"Simon?"

"Um...yeah?"

"Explain."

"Well....I might of *accidently* told her she needed to bark at baklava or it would....melt her face off."

"You MIGHT have or you DID? Uh...never mind, obviously, you did. You know what? You should watch it with those practical jokes. You never know when I might decide to pull one on you." "That would be great! You know, mom, you should lighten up....practical jokes never hurt anyone...I mean, try it one time, you'll see...it's fun...." I was trying to make her see how funny I really was.

She smiled so I kind of knew I wasn't really in trouble...then she winked at me and said, "Simon?"

"Yeah, Mom?"

Took another bite of my sandwich.

"You just ate a lamb intestines."

I stopped chewing.

"Wai...wha??"

"Yep. Lamb guts. They take all of their organs, like the hearts, lungs, liver, you know, all that stuff? Then they wrap it all in this rubbery, tubey stuff that their poop goes through. And then they cook it, cut it up in little chunks and put it on bread. I wasn't going to tell you because I thought you'd freak out but you know, since you love to joke around, I thought you'd think it was funny. And you know something? You're right. It is fun."

"So...this is a joke? Did I just eat lamb poop tubes or not???"

"Oh, Simon...you know the greatest thing about practical jokes? You never know when the joke ends and the truth begins. How does it feel when the shoe is on the other foot?"

Oh...no. She was trying to teach me a lesson. Or prove a point. Or whatever else she does that is supposed to make me "think about what I've done." All I really wanted to know was if I needed to go puke in the bathroom or not...and she wasn't telling me.

Chapter 7

After lunch, we waited a few minutes for the shuttle. Who had mellowed out a little; well, a lot, actually. My mom said she had a caffeine crash and we all hoped the little weirdo would sleep on the shuttle.

The beach we went to was in a little town called Kilyos. It was packed with people and there were umbrellas stuck in the sand everywhere. The water was really cold, which felt super good since the shuttle didn't have air conditioning and I was still feeling sweaty and sick to my stomach after the whole lunch thing.

My mom told me not to worry, that everyone in Turkey ate these sandwiches. That didn't make me feel any better about eating guts, but whatever.

The guy driving the shuttle spoke English and he told us about the Black Sea. He said it used to be a lake but a long time ago the water rose from the Mediterranean and it spilled over into the sea, making it kind of a salty lake. I started combining the words lake and sea...SEKE? LASEA? Huh. I'd have to work on that.

The cool thing he said was how the combination of kind of salty seawater and the fresh lake water meant there weren't very many fish that could eat up shipwrecks. There were lots of ancient shipwrecks in the Black Sea, some of them thousands of years old.

I was hoping my mom would let me learn how to scuba dive so I could check it out on my own but the guy said it was way too cold and it was really deep and then my mom started talking about how I might explode and I was only ten and if I wanted to do that when I was 18 she wouldn't have any say in it but right now we were just going to put our feet in the water.

Ugh.

He also talked about phytoplankton blooms, which I didn't really know anything about, but I heard the word plankton and started thinking about Spongebob and missing home. I was hoping this trip would get better because so far I had gotten in trouble twice, had eaten poop tubes and found out I wouldn't even be swimming. The town was pretty cool...lots of little stores and boats that were parked all along the beach…there were guys selling fish right out of their boat.

Who started bugging my mom right away about swimming.

"Let's find a nice spot…look…there's a little patch of sand right over there…"my mom pointed to the beach. I didn't see what she was talking about but I think she was just trying to shut Who up.

I didn't know what patch my mom was talking about because we walked a long time before we finally sat down. This place was busy. I was pretty sure our hotel had a pool so I really didn't understand why we were here…I mean, we lived kind of by a beach at home.

"Simon? Simon?"

"Yeah?"

"You really need to take this in…this sea has such history…so many legends, stories…I bet pirates even sailed these waters! Woooo Wooooo" She started to shake her hands back and forth, like she was trying to freak me out. I

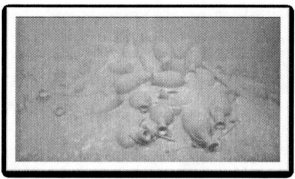

swear, it doesn't matter what country we are in, my mom can speak dork.

"Actually...there was an ancient Greek shipping vessel discovered not long ago...they found huge pots of old fish bones, remnants of olive oil...you can probably Google it and see pictures..." my dad said.

With that, they spread out a big towel and plopped down. My mom started putting sunscreen all over Who and kept telling me about how important it was for me to 'absorb my surroundings.'

I looked around. Saw a kid about my age walking out of the water with a surfboard. He looked pretty cool…I started wondering if he'd teach me how to surf.

"Mom?"

"Yes?"

"Where's the bathroom?"

"Come with me, Simon…I need to hit the john, too." I never knew why my dad said that. Sometimes he said 'hit the head'. He used to say "use the crap catcher" until Who came along..then he stopped saying that because who was repeating everything we used to say and it made my mom embarrassed to be at the store and hear Who ask to go to the crap catcher. That's when she really wanted us to start saying "potty". I didn't know what was wrong with "bathroom" but whatever.

When we got back, I saw Who talking to the surfboard kid. She was pointing to me and dancing around. I was too far away to hear what she was saying but knowing her, I knew it wouldn't be good. I started to feel nervous.

When I got closer, I could hear Who singing.

"Sissy sissy bo bissy banana fana mo missy fee fi fo missy SISSY!"

Oh no.

I looked at her.

I looked at my mom, who obviously thought this was sooooo cute.

I waved at him and kind of smiled, hoping he wouldn't care that my sister was an idiot.

"Hey…so, you're name's Missy Sissy?" He kind of smiled. And he spoke perfect English.

"Ha! No, my name is Simon…you know little sisters" and I spun my finger around the side of my head so he'd know she was crazy.

"No! his name IS Sissy!" then Who grabbed my around my waist and tried to lift her feet up…she was stuck on me like a wart.

I looked at my mom, who didn't seem to think this was a problem.

"I'm Jake...we're visiting from California...."
Perfect.

"Say, Jake...why don't you show Simon some of your fancy surf board moves?"
This couldn't get any worse. First Who calls me Missy Sissy and now my mom was acting like I was a three year old who needed to be entertained by the cool California surfer kid.
"OK...you have a board?"

"Uh, no...I left it back home..."

"No you dinint, Sissy. You don't have a surp bode. Remember?"

"Yeah...yeah, I do....you just don't know about it...shut up...." I glared at Who.

"Let's go down to the edge...we can take turns on my board if you want."

"Sure..."

We started to walk toward the edge of the water. Jake handed me his board.

"You can go first."

I had no idea what to do. The only surfing I had seen was on Spongebob, the Big Kahuna episode. I was in trouble. I walked out until the water was about to my waist. It was freezing. I was trying to figure out what to do when a huge wave came. It flipped me upside down; I let go of Jake's board, and the next thing I knew I was crawling out of the water, with seaweed in my hair and sand in my butt crack.

Jake was chasing his board down the beach.

"Simon Sez!"

I choked out water.

"Yeah?"

"What were you thinking?? I turn my back for a minute and you're out in the middle of the Black Sea??? Do you have any idea what could of happened???" my mom was losing it.

Just then, Jake came back.

"Got it!" He smiled.

But my mom wasn't done.

"Don't forget, mister, you are the one who wanted to be done with swimming lessons. You only graduated the Tough Turtles class! You never even tried the Daring Dolphins, so don't think for one minute you're going in the Black Sea like it's the swimming pool!"

I don't know why she kept saying 'Black Sea'...like the name was supposed to make it scarier or something. But that wasn't the worst.

Jake was cracking up.

"Jake?"

"Yes?"

"Perhaps you and Simon can make some sand castles? You can borrow Who's beach toys." When my mom said things like that, it wasn't a question; it was more like 'this is what you're going to do.'

"um....sand castles? Nah, I think I'm going back out."

40

He looked at me and smiled.
"See ya, Tough Turtle."

Chapter 8

A few days later, my mom told me I'd be going to a local school to see what it was like. I was NOT happy about this little tradition, but every time we went somewhere, she would fix it so I could spend a day in some random school with kids I didn't know who thought I was a weirdo.

I didn't learn anything and usually the lunches were as bad as the hot lunches back home.

"Come on! We don't want to be late! Did you brush your teeth? You don't want to be the stinky breath kid from Seattle, you know." My mom winked at me.

Ugh.
"Oh, Simon?"

"Yeah?" I said with a mouthful of toothpaste.

"You can't wear that. In Turkey, the children wear uniforms. They are making an exception and letting you visit them in only the shirt and tie...it's on the table. .."

"Mom? Seriously? You get how hot it is, right? You want me to wear that shirt with a tie to school when I'm supposed to be on vacation?"

As soon as I said it, I regretted it. Here we go...

"Simon, lest you forget, we are NOT on vacation...I am working and YOU are supposed to be on what your teachers and I have decided to call educational international field trips. Part of this is visiting a school and getting a feel for what a day is like in the life of the student in that country...why do we have to go over this every time???"

"Fine. But I don't know how to do the tie."

Chapter 9

The school was pretty much like mine, only they all had to wear uniforms. Instead of being spread out, it was only as long as a few school buses, but about 4 stories tall. We were able to see where we were going because they had signs written in Turkish and English. So we found the office right away.

"Hello! This is Simon…we chatted on the phone about him visiting a class today?"

"Ah yes! Hello, Simon!" the lady behind the desk came rushing around, and gave me a kiss on each cheek. One thing I noticed about this country, they were really friendly and the ladies always wanted to kiss me and Who. I didn't kiss back, though, I just stood there.

"Hi.."

"Today is a great day to visit the school! We are having what I believe you call a 'field trip' to the Sultanahmet and the Hippodrome!"

I looked at my mom and waited for her to explain what this lady was talking about, but my mom looked just as confused as me.

"Did I forget to mention that? Yes, I must have...well, the primary children are going to the Sultan Ahmet...you might know it as The Blue Mosque for the day...it's just beautiful...you'll really enjoy it!
I could tell my mom wasn't happy about this; she thought she'd leave me at the school for a few hours, where I'd magically soak up all this Turkish school stuff and then pick me up. No way was she going to let me go...which was fine with me, because I didn't want to be there anyway.

"Mom?"

"Yes?"

"I don't think this is such a good idea...I mean, I'm sure there will be lots of people...what if I got lost?" I knew she'd freak out. She looked at me like she was trying to figure out what I was doing. Then she kind of smiled and nodded her head. "You know, Simon, the Hippodrome is world famous. Why do you think that is?"

"I don't know...because it looks like a hippos butt?" I laughed. She didn't.

"No...because it has man eating hippos in it. Only place in the world."

The school lady looked confused, like she didn't understand what my mom was saying even though she spoke really good English.

I looked at my mom.

She looked back at me.

I knew right away what was happening.

She wasn't going to let me go.

She wanted me to experience it.

She was coming with me.

Great. Now I got to deal with not only being the weird kid who is just visiting, but I get to be the weird kid who's mom is all excited and wants to tag along.

"Hippos are vegetarians. I know that for sure." I told her.

"Oh, Simon, maybe hippos in the states are vegetarians, but in Turkey? They'll bite your hand right off!!" Then she made her eyes get really big and made her mouth start biting the air, clacking her teeth together.
The office lady looked SUPER confused now.

"Ma'am? I can assure you...the hippodrome doesn't have hippos...we just call it that..."

"Oh, I know..I'm just teasing Simon. But I think I'll come along, if that's all right? It sounds like a fun outing!"

I knew it. My mom had gone to every single field trip of my life. No way was she going to let me go on one outside the country.

The bus ride wasn't very long. I could see the building we were going to pretty much the whole time, it was so big. There were six tower things and a big building that looked like a bubble. When we got there, I saw how huge it was. There was a big fountain in front of it and it took a long time to get in. There were little tiles all over the ceiling on the inside, with little pictures. My mom was losing it. It was pretty cool, it was super old...I like things that are really old. I like to think about all the people who have been there before.

We had to take our shoes off and my mom had to borrow a scarf thing for her head before she went into the mosque because that's the rules or something.

The inside was really big and the tiles that made pictures all over the ceiling were blue.

"Oh, Simon?" The teacher asked me.

Great. Every time I went on one of these guest field trips, the teachers always thought they needed to include me. That usually meant they'd ask me a bunch of questions and the other kids would look at me like I was a dork.

"Yes?"

"Did you know French visitors called turquoise the color of the Turks because of the Blue Mosque?"

"Nope...didn't know that." All the kids were looking at me. They looked pretty bored, probably because they had seen this place a million times. Like when we have company from out of town and we go to the Space Needle. It's cool and all, but after going a ton of times, it gets a little boring. My mom was freaking out the way our out of town guests do when we take them to the Pike Place Market and they watch the guys catch the fish.

After we left the Blue Mosque, we went to the Hippodrome. It was kind of like a field, only it had three really old things in it. One was from Egypt and it was over 3,000 years old...it kind of looked like the Washington Monument, only a lot smaller and it was covered in those hieroglyphics the ancient Egyptians used, like in the Scooby Doo movie where they went to Egypt.

(It really was pretty cool)

Chapter 10

We were there most of the day and when we got back to the hotel, my dad and Who were just coming in from lunch.

Who was dancing around the hotel room like a lunatic.

"Mommy! Guess what???"

"What, my little sugar cookie?"

"We saw a-most nakkie wadies at lunch!"

My mom looked at my dad with the same look she had when I lost her keys a few months ago.

"What?"
Before my dad could say anything, Who pushed her shirt up and started to wiggle around like she had a rash or something.

"Yeah! Like this, Mommy...look at me!" then she started to really wiggle around.

I looked at my dad. I bet he was in trouble but he just laughed.

"Yes, the restaurant we went to had belly dancers. Who got quite a kick out of it." He winked at me.

"How'd it go at the school today?" my dad asked.

"It was pretty cool...we went on a field trip to the Blue Mosque...or they also call it the Sultan Ahmet...they have lots of cool, old stuff there....they even had these really tall towers like the one Fiona was locked in..." I looked at Who, who kept wiggling around.

My dad laughed. "Well, next week we are going to check out one of the oldest ruins in the world...Ephesus...REALLY old stuff...I think you'll like it."

With that he started to dance with Who. Weirdos.

Chapter 11

Over the next few days, my mom met with the rug lady and my dad took us to some of the local stores and shops.
We rode a ferry and ate fish sandwiches sold right off of boats. They weren't as good as Filet o Fishes from McDonalds but they were still pretty good.

My mom finished her research on the rug lady a lot sooner than she thought which meant we got to see more stuff. One of the first places she wanted to see was Cappadocia, the place she told me about when I was eating that lamb poop tube sandwich.

We rented a car and drove a long ways to get there. I thought it was a town but it's actually an area with lots of little towns in it. We went to one called Goreme. It looked just like my mom described...like the moon, but also it had these carved in rooms and rocks that looked like gigantic arrows. They're called fairy chimneys.

I started to tell Who that this was where Tinker Bell's ancestors lived when my mom gave me that look that meant I should shut up. Was it my fault they were called fairy chimneys? I didn't name them. And who knows, maybe Tinker Bell's ancestors DID come from here. My mom wasn't buying it and had to spend about twenty minutes calming Who down, because she was

convinced she would see fairies.

Stupid kid.

We pulled into a parking lot and I noticed a huge hot air balloon lying on its side, being filled up with air.

"Ready? We're going to see Cappadocia from a hot air balloon!"

Except for all that candy the old lady gave us, this seemed like the best idea my mom had come up with. The four of us walked into a little basket thing and just a few minutes later, the balloon was pointing straight up and we took off, over the cool rocks. Who could barely see over the edge of the basket and my mom started to look like she might pass out because the balloon kept going higher and higher and higher.

"Simon? Don't be nervous."
"Me? I'm not nervous, mom. Are you?"

"Oh, of course not. Why? Do I look nervous?"

"Um, yeah."

My mom was standing in the middle of the basket, and the heat thing that was making the air hot was right above her head...she kind of looked like that one character from the Christmas show, Mr. Heat Miser.

It's a pretty old show, but my mom always makes me watch it every year when the Christmas shows are one…Frosty the Snowman, Charlie Brown Christmas with that little tree and of course Rudolph. Not like it's a bad thing, but whenever those shows are on, every year she says the same things, tells me how much she loved them, how she watched them when she was a kid and how things have changed so much.

I decided not to tell her she looked like that heat guy cause she kept biting her lip and looking all over the place, like she was waiting for a giant arrow to poke our balloon and she was trying to figure out how she would save me and Who.

57

There were lots of other balloons, which was cool because the ground and hills were sand colored. Flying over it was one of the coolest things I've ever done. I could see all of these little houses and rooms that had been carved into the mountain thousands of years ago.
Like a city in the mountains. People still lived in some of them and there were a few hotels in there, too.

"What you are looking at is a collection of cave houses, or troglodyte dwellings. They have been around for over a thousand years. The landscape is often called a moonscape because it looks so much like the moon!" The hot air balloon guide spoke in a pretty thick accent but I could still understand him enough to know that was pretty impressive. Thinking that there were people over a thousand years ago who carved whole underground villages out of these mountains was cool.

"Below you will see the fairy chimneys...they are an extraordinary example of the powerful natural resources of the world, such as water, wind and volcanoes. They were formed millions of years ago and got their name because ancient people believed they were at once time inhabited by fairies."

I looked at Who. Her eyes were popping out of her head. Of course.

My mom had started to calm down a little, but I noticed she still had one hand on my shoulder and one hand on Who's shoulder.

My dad was videotaping everything. Maybe if the air came out of our balloon he'd film us smashing into a fairy chimney...then I could save everyone by climbing down it and catching them all as they jumped out of the basket. Then I'd be on the news and that Booger Welsh would be sooo jealous that I was famous and he was just stupid.

We didn't crash land, though. We just kept floating over Goreme, looking at the houses, churches, fairy chimneys and a lot of other balloons.

I needed to pee and wondered what would happen if someone peed from a hot air balloon. I decided I wouldn't try it though.   I had a feeling my mom wouldn't think it was as funny as me.

Chapter 12

"Simon?"

"Yeah?"

"Guess where we're going today?" my mom asked.

"I dunno...where?" I mumbled. I was still kind of sleepy and lying in bed with my eyes shut. Who had turned on the lights to I pulled the blanket over my head.

"To see where Santa Claus was born!"

The minute she said that I knew my chances of going back to sleep were over. Who jumped onto the bed and grabbed me by both ears.

"SISSY!!!! WAKE UP!!!!"

"OK..I'm up..." then I pulled the covers totally over my face and tried to go back to sleep.

"SISSY!!!"

"Simon?   You really do need to get up. We are going to a place called Patara, which is the birthplace of St. Nicholas....aka Santa Claus! Ho ho ho!!" My mom seemed like she was as excited as Who.

I could tell by the way she was talking, our trip to Patara wasn't really about seeing where Santa was born, but more about it being a place that had a really nice beach.

"Simon?"

"Yeah?"

"Did you hear what I said? About Patara Beach being voted one of the best beaches in the world? In the world, Simon. Isn't that something?"

"Yeah, Mom.   I heard you. You said it about 10 times already." I was hoping I could sleep on the way but Who kept pinching my nose closed every time I shut my eyes.

My mom was too busy thinking about that dumb beach to notice so I knew I'd have to deal with this on my own.

"Who?" I whispered.

"What, Sissy?"

"If you keep pinching my nose, I'm going to tell Santa. He won't be happy with you. I bet he'll give you a big box of underwear…and NOT the kind with princesses, just the plain kind. That's all you'll get. Just underwear." I kept whispering but then I winked at Who so she would think I was on her side.

"Ohhhh, oh-tay, Sissy. Will we see Rudolf?"

"We might, but since he's in Turkey, you have to say it the Turkish way…Poodolf."

"Weally? Poodolf? Like poop?"

"Yep. Poodolf. Now, just be quiet and think about what you want to say to Santa..maybe he'll let you ride on Poodolf."

Who acted like a perfect angel for the whole drive, probably because she thought she'd be able to talk to Santa directly and tell him everything she wanted.

Chapter 13

When we got to Patara, my mom started looking around for North Pole stuff to shut Who up.

There was nothing.

"Mommy? Where's Santa's house?" Who asked.

"Um, I'm not sure yet..." I could tell my mom was kind of freaked out, because she had been talking to Who about Santa for the last hour. "I can't believe they don't have something for tourists..."

We drove around some more, but all we saw was a really nice beach and lots of ruins. No elves. No fat dude in a red suit in front of a candy house. Nothing.

"Mooommmyyyy???? Where is he???"

"Well...uh...Who, you know Santa was BORN here...but he LIVES in the North Pole. I thought maybe he'd have a summer home here but I guess not..."

"Really, Mom? A summer house?" I started to laugh. She was desperate.

Who was pouting. Her lip was shoved out, her arms were crossed and her eyebrows looked mad. So much for her angel act.

"I know! Let's go to the beach! It's considered one of the best beaches in the world. Did I mention that?"
On the way to the beach, we saw a ruin called the Arch of Modestus.

I read in my Turkey guide thing that it was almost two thousand years old. Some people called it a gateway to the city, but really it was just in the middle of a field. I also found out a lot of the ruins were only recently discovered because they've been under a ton of sand for a long time. The arch thing was really cool and kind of made me want to climb to the top of it, but my mom said no.

Who was still mad when we got to the beach, even though my mom had gotten her an ice cream and promised she'd write a letter to Santa herself, explaining how disappointed Who was that she didn't get to see his home while we were in Turkey.

On our way, we saw a bunch of rocks that some people think are the remnants of the world's oldest lighthouse. Since I'm so much older than Who and obviously way smarter, I was really interested in this.

She was just mad about the whole Santa thing.

We got out and walked toward the beach. I saw a deer run past and whispered to Who "hey...did you see that? I think Poodolf is out for a run."

Her eyes got super big and she screamed.

"PoooooooDooooolllffffff!!! Come back Poo-ey! I want to play with my Poo-ey!!!"

I was cracking up. There were other people at the beach who obviously knew enough English to know it sounded like my sister wanted to play with her poop. Oh, I was probably going to get in trouble for this one but it was so funny, I started to think it would be totally worth it.

"Who?! What's going on???" My mom started to chase after Who, because she had started chasing after Poo. Heh heh.

Finally, my mom had to just drop all of the beach stuff she had brought and started to really run after my sister. I don't know if she was running after her because she was nervous about her falling, or drowning, or whatever moms worry about or if it was because my stupid sister kept screaming at the top of her lungs how much she wanted to pet her poo, love her poo, snuggle with her poo...you know, things like that. My dad didn't even ask what was going on. He just shook his head and sat down on a piece of driftwood.

"You know...if you have anything to do with your sister chasing after a deer and screaming about poop, you're probably going to be in big trouble, right?" my dad asked.

I smiled.

"Yeah. I know."

"Worth it?"

"Yep." And I laughed so hard I farted.

Chapter 14

"Simon?" my mom had that tone in her voice. I knew something was up.

"Yeah?"

"Have you written about any of the sights you have seen since we've been here?" she asked.

"Well...no. I'm not sure what I want to write about. I've been taking pictures, though." I hoped that would be enough to make her stop asking me. I loved to travel but I hated the whole writing about it part. It's part of the agreement between my mom and the school...I get to go on these trips as long as I write a big long thing about it for my teachers to see. Sometimes they even make me do presentations on my trip. My mom always gets a bunch of postcards and buys food and stuff to bring back for the classroom. I noticed she bought a bunch of boxes of Turkish Delight so I figured that would be what I was bringing back to my class.

"Well, we've seen a lot. Tomorrow we are going to Ephesus. I want you to do some research on my laptop so you can be fully prepared for your visit. I know! You can call it your Emphasis on Ephesus!" My mom was a dork.

Chapter 15

Because there was so much to see, we were
going to spend two days in Ephesus before
leaving Turkey. I knew I would have to get this
whole report thing going or my mom would not
stop bugging me about it.

There were two things I found out that I thought
were cool. One, that there was a carving of
some lady called Nike and she was the ancient
lady of victory or something like that, and I think
she's the reason Nike, the shoes, named
themselves Nike. I always wondered that,
because who's ever heard of a kid named Nike?
Or a place? Or food? So that was cool. But it
made me wonder about the other shoe names. I
know that Adidas stood for All Day I Dream
About Spaghetti. That's what I think, anyway.

The other thing I learned was there is a really old
temple that has the Medusa carved into the area
above the entrance. They put it there to keep
bad things from happening to it. Something like
that. I thought it was cool because once my
mom dressed up as Medusa for Halloween. The
carving of Medusa didn't really look like she had

snake hair, like the REAL lady, though. It just looked curly.

Once we parked, there was a lot of walking to do. This place was huge. I had my camera and some paper so I could take notes on whatever I liked so I could write about it for my dumb report.

"Simon? I REALLY want you to pay attention. This is the most well preserved ancient Roman city today. There are so many things to see, you don't want to miss a thing!" My mom smiled at me.

"I know, I know." I looked at Who.

"Simon? No monkey business. I mean it. Don't try to trick your sister into thinking those snakes on Medusas head are going to come alive or that

there are going to be dead bodies coming out of the sarcophagi. I'm serious."
"Wait. Out of the what?" I asked.

"The sarcophagi. That's plural. Or sarcophagus..that's the singular use. Anyway, it's a stone coffin, usually with really intricate carvings on it. Seriously. Really. I mean it. NO MESSING WITH YOUR SISTER. Understand?"

"ok, ok. I get it." Jeez. I think my mom was still mad about the whole Poodolf thing.

As we walked, I noticed there were tiles floors just sort of all over the place, kind of like they were just dropped there for no reason. Our tour guide told us those were the remains of people's homes. The floors to the houses were still there, but the walls and roofs weren't.

The guide started talking about the Temple of Artemis. He was making a really big deal about it, too. Saying it was one of the seven ancient wonders of the world. As we were walking, he passed around a picture of what it looked like. It had lots of columns and looked really big.

I was pretty excited to see it. Then I saw the REAL thing.

Yep. One column left. How was I supposed to write about this place if there was nothing left to write about?

My mom just laughed when I tried to talk to her about it.

"Just be patient. There are so many things to see. Trust me."

We got a little closer and I noticed there were a few people near the one column. There was a man, taller than my dad, and it didn't even look like he was as tall as the first stone on the column. Huh. That thing must have been huge before it was destroyed.

We kept walking. Who was being pushed because she had a stroller. I started to think about how much that sucked. Not that I wanted a stroller or anything, but it would be nice to be pushed around instead of walking so much all the time.

I did notice the road we were walking on had big chunks out of it, but I thought that was just from age. I heard someone in our tour group say it was done on purpose when they did the roads so

75

the people walking on them wouldn't slip in the rain. We have fake marble in our upstairs bathroom and I've fallen a few times so that made sense.

"We're coming up on the Library of Celsus" the tour guy said.

Great. Now, not only did I have to take notes and remember this stuff for my dumb report, I had to go to a library? This trip was getting worse by the second.

I was not expecting to see what I saw. I mean, I knew I was in an old place and I had seen ruins before, but nothing like this. It was almost two thousand years old. There were statues in front and the guide guy said it was named after some guy named Celsus. I took a picture of that because I thought for sure the librarian at my school would think it was cool. It didn't look like the ones I was used to...for one thing, it didn't have walls, just the front. Well, and it didn't have books.

The tour guide told our group Celsus was buried in a sarcophagus underneath the library. My mom elbowed me in the ribs.

"Ow! What??" I asked, and rubbed my side.

"Aren't you glad we talked about what a sarcophagus is? You know what he's talking about!" She looked so happy with herself. Like I wouldn't have figured out what it was when I heard the guy was buried in it. Well, maybe I would have thought it was a mummy wrap thing. Maybe.

We kept walking and exploring. Sometimes, people just didn't say anything, they were so surprised by how much was there.

We stayed at a hotel that night and were up super early the next day to see the rest of Ephesus.

We got together with the same group and started walking again. Except Who, of course.

"How many of you know about the archeological findings of Ephesus?"
A few people in our group raised their hands.

"Well, it is estimated that only 15% of this extraordinary city has been excavated. That means there are still so many things yet to discover!"

People were talking about that when we finally got to the point where we could see the stadium.

It was hard to believe they had stadiums that were kind of like the ones now days. I mean, when I was walking down the road to that, it looked like a regular stadium.

I was wondering if they had football back then when the guide started talking about how, a long, long time ago, it was where the gladiators fought.

I never told my mom, but one time my grandma let me watch a movie called Gladiator and it was so cool. The guy gets kicked out of the army and has to be a gladiator and he fights with animals and other really strong guys, until someone dies. I knew my mom would freak out if she knew my grandma had let me and Who watch Gladiator so I couldn't say anything but inside I was freaking out. THIS WAS THE COOLEST PLACE EVER. I wanted to spend the rest of the day here. Don't get me wrong, it wasn't like I wanted to pretend to be a gladiator or anything, but it was really cool to walk around on the same ground gladiators had fought thousands of years ago.

Our time there was pretty short but we saw a few more sights kind of like the stadium. A few theaters where they had plays and politicians spoke, stuff like that.

My mom had gotten us each an ice cream from a little cart, called dondurma. It was the orchid ice cream I had heard about and it was weird. Not frozen, but cold. Not soft, but kind of chewy. Who and I were busy trying to figure this stuff out when my parents decided to read some of the plaques around one of the ruins. At this point, even though every thing was really cool, it started to all look the same.

"Simon, I want you to watch Who while we read some of these, ok? No funny business, just eat your ice cream and hang out for ten minutes, alright?"

"Sure." I looked around and realized we were by a whole row of ancient toilets.

They didn't have doors, or anything. I guess back then you just sat and took care of business. I also noticed there wasn't any place for toilet paper. I wonder what they used? I made a note on my paper to look that up, because THAT would be interesting. I guess I always thought toilet paper was around but now I think I was wrong about that.

"Sissy? I have to potty." Who had dropped her ice cream and was doing that dance move that means she has to pee.

Great.

I looked around. The closest real bathroom was a long walk back and NO WAY was I going to carry Who, especially if there was even a chance she'd pee on me. There weren't any bushes, either.

"Sisssssyyyy...I have to go weally bad..." she started to whine.

Oh well.

I plopped her on top of one of those holes and told her to potty. I mean, the ancient Romans did it, why not her?

She started to sing a song about pee and kick her legs. Just then, my mom came back. I think that if she didn't have veins and stuff attached to her eyes, they probably would have fallen out of her head.

"Mommy! I went pee pee on the rock hole!"

My mom was busy pulling Who's pants up and giving me THE look.

"Simon. I told you specifically not to mess with your sister. I leave you alone for five minutes and I find her urinating on a piece of ancient history? In front of strangers??"

"Mom, I didn't have a choice. I mean, it is a toilet, right?"

"Yes, Simon, but it's also a treasured ruin. And you let your sister PEE ON IT."

"Well, technically she peed IN it."

My mom shook her head. Our visit to Ephesus was over. We were heading back home in a few days.

"I hope you got enough for your report." My mom said on our way back to Istanbul.

"Yeah, I think I did."

"You know, in a few months we will be taking a short trip to Vietnam…and I swear, Simon…"

"What?" I asked, innocently.

"You know what? Never mind. Work on your report, we have a long drive back."

"OK..." I started to look at my notes and go through some of the pictures I had taken.

"Simon? Do me a favor, ok?" my mom asked.

"What, Mom?"

"No more public urination."

My dad and I both looked at her like she was crazy.

She held up both hands.

"At least not on historical, ancient or sacred places...deal?"

I smiled at her. "Deal."

"So...Vietnam?" I asked.

"Yep. Excited?" my mom asked.

"Yeah! They have those really good sandwiches I like, remember?"

"Yes, I do remember, but what do you know about the country?"

"Um…that they make really good sandwiches?"

My mom laughed and put her arm around me. "Yes. They make good sandwiches. I guess we'll find out the rest when we get there, huh?"

I didn't know what to expect but I knew it wouldn't be anything like Turkey. Turkey was cool. Lamb guts sandwiches and all.

Coming Soon!!

Book Two - Simon Goes to Vietnam

Book Three – Simon Goes to Scotland

Book Four – Simon Goes to Australia

Book Five – Simon Goes to India

A word from the author –

Thank you, so much, for getting to know Simon
and Who. I hope they made you laugh and learn
about other cultures and countries!

Please check out my website –
www.andrea-wetzel.com to learn about my other
projects. Thanks!